WHAT IS RIGHT FOR TULIP...

WHAT IS RIGHT FOR TULIP...

by Roger Duvoisin

ALFRED · A · KNOPF, NEW YORK

To Harry Rodman

From morning to night
there are many things to be done.
Some do them like this, some like that,
and all do as best they can.
But what is right for Tulip
may not be right for you!

GOOD MORNING. It's time to get up and wash.

Tulip the polar bear thinks icy water is just right for his bath.

But Cotton the cat prefers no water at all.

The elephant *is* his own shower.

And Bill in his shower, with warm water and soap, with a washcloth and a brush, makes himself clean and neat to be ready for school.

BREAKFAST. Everyone is hungry.
The crocodiles are often *too* hungry!

6

Raccoon has found the breakfast he likes best.

Mary says that Bill eats like Day the dog and
Cotton the cat, but she is teasing him.

Bill sits straight at the breakfast table, with
a fork and a knife, with a spoon and a glass,
and eats like a gentleman.

GOOD AFTERNOON. Let's greet visitors.
Bees greet them with stings.

Day might have *too much* love for visitors.

The rhinoceros does not trust visitors.
He would rather see them up a tree.

But Mary loves her friends and greets them with a kiss.

PLEASE HELP YOURSELF. It is good to
share what we have.
Dragons did like to share, sometimes.

But hens never do.

Foxes do not know that the wise man said,
"He who will not share ends up with nothing."

But Mary will even share her dear
cat Cotton with her friends.

HAVE FUN. It's playing time.
Cotton has a favorite game.

And so does Day's puppy.

To play jokes on friends is great fun for Tulip.

Bill doesn't play jokes. He plays with scissors
and colored paper to make his own animal friends.

NOW IT'S GOOD NIGHT.

The crocodile closes his eyes and floats off to sleep.

The hedgehog sleeps too, and he does not need
a "Do not disturb" sign.

Tulip chooses the bed he likes best and drops off to sleep.

Bill and Mary, in their gay bedrooms, put on
their pajamas and lie in their soft beds with warm quilts
and pillows and their favorite toys. And they fall
asleep after calling, "Good night! Good night!"

Text set in Perpetua

Printed by Reehl Litho., Inc., New York, N.Y.

Bound by A. Horowitz & Son, Bookbinders, Clifton, N.J.